# KBOOOM!

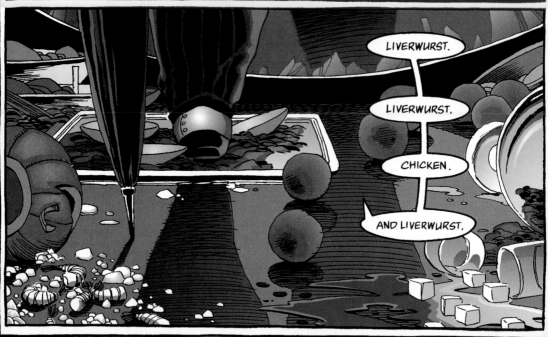

LIVERWURST.

LIVERWURST.

CHICKEN.

AND LIVERWURST.

While attending another in the endless array of charitable functions I endure...

...the unexpected happens with a terrible swiftness.

The grand entrance is _intentional._

I want Penguin's attention focused only on _me._

Hopefully, minimalizing the casualties to _one--_

--the Penguin _himself_.

AHH,,,THE BATMAN.

WHILE I HAVE AN **AFFECTION** FOR MOST FLYING CREATURES--

--THE WINGED RAT IS **NOT** AMONG THEM.

DROP THE GUN.

NOW.

The demand was unnecessary.

The singular solution is striking _quickly_.

Relentlessly.

Some would say...

...savagely.

Innocent lives are at stake.

Almost any _means_ justifies the ends.

WHEN PARTAKING IN PURE FISTICUFFS--

--YOU HAVE ME AT A DISADVANTAGE.

AND RATHER THAN SUFFER THE INDIGNITY OF ANOTHER DEFEAT-

--I'LL TAKE MY LEAVE.

GOOD-BYE, CRUEL WORLD!

A cobalt-driven single-stroke portable jet engine. Capable of accelerating to a three G-force.

Alfred informed me of the theft of a prototype from Gotham's Primatek Laboratories while updating the computer.

The Penguin's uncooperative choice is not unexpected.

His overinflated ego defines his actions--

--limiting his ability to see the reasonable alternative--

--and leading to an extremely painful conclusion.

It is a luxury I cannot afford for myself.

Wayne Manor.

My father's home.

No matter how long I live here, I will always think of it as that.

An excuse will have to be provided for my... disappearance from the fund-raiser.

Alfred will come up with something.

He always does.

HMMM...

TIRED.

...VERY TIRED.

DID YOU LOSE YOUR KEYS, SIR?

OR DID YOU MERELY WISH TO MAKE CERTAIN I WAS AWAKE AT THIS HOUR?

ALFRED...

CAN I INTEREST YOU IN A FRESH BOWL OF CONSOMMÉ, MASTER BRUCE?

I IMAGINE THEY ONLY HAD THAT ODOROUS LIVERWURST PATÉ EVERYONE SEEMS TO BE SERVING.

SHRIMP.

YOU HAVEN'T TAKEN TO NAME-CALLING, HAVE YOU, SIR?

OR ARE YOU REFERRING TO THE MENU?

I ... WOULDN'T HAVE THOUGHT TO SERVE SHELLFISH AT THIS TIME OF YEAR.

NOW THAT YOU MENTION IT, I MIGHT'VE EATEN SOMETHING --

--THAT DIDN'T AGREE WITH ME.

IF YOU *PROMISE* THAT YOU WON'T BE TRAIPSING OUT AGAIN THIS EVENING --

--I'LL SEE TO IT YOU ARE NOT DISTURBED UNTIL MORNING.

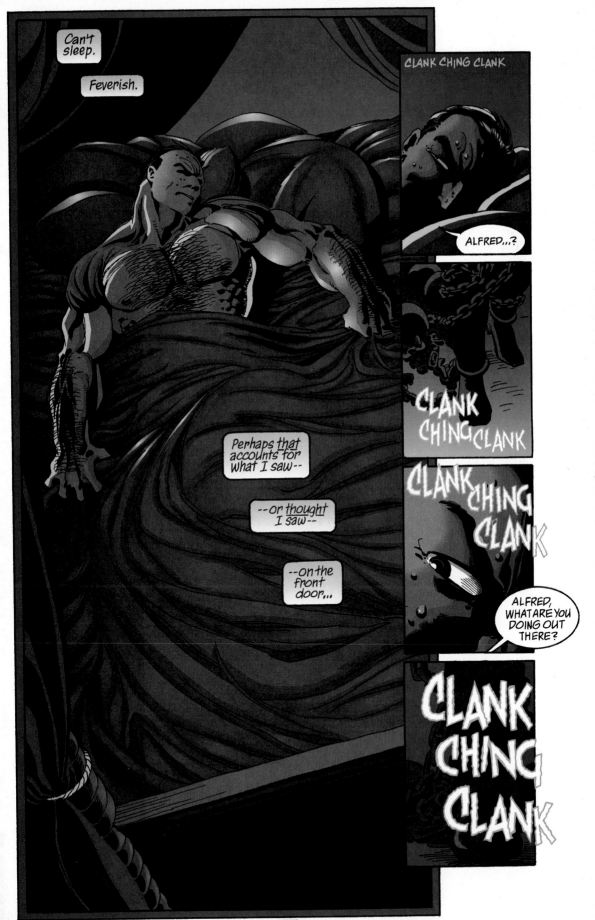

**NO!**

Do not waste the brief time we have by denying my existence before you.

Look, instead, long and hard at the weight I carry now.

These chains I wear I forged in life.

Link by link, yard by yard, I made this burden.

Obsessed with my medical practice, I lost sight of what was truly important.

THIS IS SOMEONE'S IDEA OF A HALLOWEEN JOKE--

--A PERVERSE PRANK!

YOU'RE **WRONG!** MY FATHER SAVED LIVES!

HE WAS A GREAT MAN!

Bruce...

I have risked much by coming to you and have done so out of love.

I pray I am not too late.

Your obsession with **Batman**--

--creates an even greater and more thunderous chain!

19

Tonight, beginning when the clock strikes "one"--

--you will be visited by the first of three spirits.

Heed their warnings, my son.

HEED THEIR WARNINGS!

HOW DARE YOU...!

HOW DARE YOU BREAK INTO MY HOME--

--DEFILE THE MEMORY OF MY FATHER!

I... I've been dreaming.

The fever.

There is no other explanation...

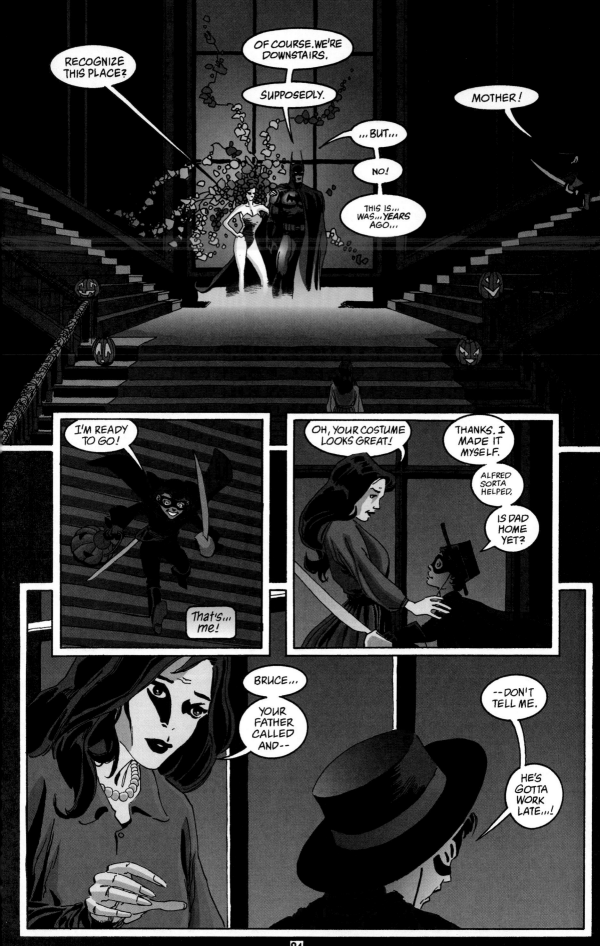

IT'S NOT FAIR!

HE *PROMISED* HE WOULD TAKE ME TRICK OR TREATING!

HE PROMISED...

I KNOW,

BUT THERE WAS AN *EMERGENCY* ...

THERE'S *ALWAYS* SOME EMERGENCY!

YOUR DAD WANTED TO BE THERE -- IF HE COULD, ONLY--

BATMAN.

THEY CANNOT SEE OR HEAR YOU.

I'M GONNA WAIT FOR HIM.

EVEN IF IT TAKES *ALL NIGHT!*

BRUCE, I COULD TAKE YOU OUT MYSELF.

OR, WE CAN CALL SOME OF THE *OTHER* CHILDREN AT SCHOOL AND GO OUT WITH THEM.

SHE ... DOESN'T KNOW ...

YOU DO.

REMEMBER?

Again... that's me!

I'd... forgotten how...

...reckless I could be back then.

Awake...!

HOME.

IN MY BED.

ALL OF IT... SOME KIND OF **NIGHTMARE**...

...THE SHRIMP I ATE...

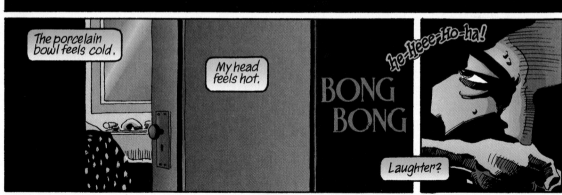

The porcelain bowl feels cold.

My head feels hot.

BONG BONG

He-Heee-Ho-ha!

Laughter?

OOO.

ROUGH-HOUSING.

MISSED ME.

MISSED ME.

NOW YOU GOTTA KISS ME.

YOU KNOW, FOR THE "WORLD'S GREATEST DETECTIVE"--

--YOU SURE ARE HAVING TROUBLE GETTING IT THROUGH YOUR *THICK SKULL* THAT YOU CAN'T *TOUCH* ME.

I MEAN, NO POINT IN BEATING A DEAD HORSE, BATTY, OLD BOY.

UNLESS, OF COURSE, YOU *LIKE* THE TASTE OF HORSE MEAT.

*Another one of those...*

*...spirits?*

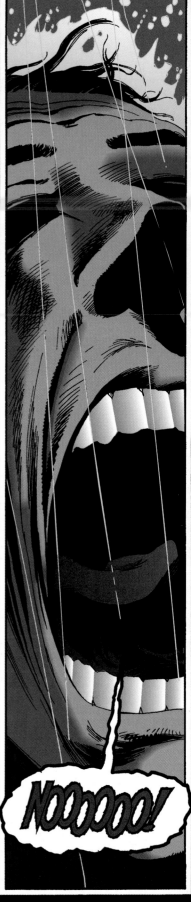

SPIRIT?

SPIRIT...

YES, I SLEPT QUITE WELL, THANK YOU.

IT WAS *YOU* WHO WENT TO BED COMPLAINING OF HAVING EATEN SOMETHING--

-- "THAT DIDN'T AGREE WITH YOU."

ALFRED!

WHAT IS THAT YOU'RE SAYING, SIR?

YOU'RE ALL RIGHT THEN!

GOTHAM

PENGUIN CAPTURE BY BATMAN

I'VE BROUGHT YOU TEA.

PLAIN TOAST.

AND AN ACCOUNT OF YET *ANOTHER* OF *BATMAN'S* THRILLING EXPLOITS.

WHAT DAY IS IT?

TODAY? WHY, IT'S *HALLOWEEN,* MASTER BRUCE.

TONIGHT WILL BE *FRAUGHT* WITH ALL SORTS OF CRIMINAL AC- TIVITY.

I ASSUME YOU'LL WANT YOUR COSTUME *PRESSED.*

ALFRED, DO *NOT* ASSUME *ANYTHING!*

*All in one night.*

Don't know what to make of it.

The spirits seem to have done their job--

--all in one night!

The library-- restored.

Everything is as it was...

...except...

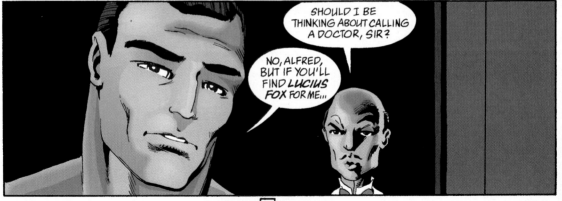

SHOULD I BE THINKING ABOUT CALLING A DOCTOR, SIR?

NO, ALFRED, BUT IF YOU'LL FIND *LUCIUS FOX* FOR ME...

...and invite him over for cocktails this afternoon...

WELL?

I'M ... SOMETHING AT A LOSS.

YOU'RE **SURE** THIS IS WHAT YOU WANT TO DO?

NEVER BEEN MORE CERTAIN OF ANYTHING.

I WANT A WAY OF KEEPING MY **NAME, REPUTATION**--

--AND THE WAYNE FORTUNE **ALIVE** IN GOTHAM CITY,

"THE WAYNE FOUNDATION."

"TO HELP THE LESS FORTUNATE."

I LIKE IT. I WANT IN.

BUT, BRUCE, ARE YOU ALL RIGHT? LAST NIGHT'S SHOOTING--

ALL I KNOW IS--

--LAST NIGHT WAS VERY SPECIAL.

O-KAY. LOOK, I HATE TO RUN OFF--

--I WANT TO SPEND HALLOWEEN WITH MY KIDS.

UNDER-STANDABLE.

BEFORE YOU GO--

--I HAVE SOMETHING THAT BELONGS TO YOU.

MY MEDALLION...?

THE **POLICE** CONTACTED ME REGARDING THE PENGUIN'S LOOT--

--AND I RECOGNIZED YOUR... PIECE AND COULDN'T RESIST RETURNING IT TO YOU **AGAIN**.

I NEVER TOLD YOU **WHY** THIS LITTLE THING MEANS SO MUCH TO ME.

IT WAS A **GIFT** FROM MY FATHER. SILLY, HUH?

NO, LUCIUS.

NOT SILLY AT ALL.

WOULDN'T YOU FEEL MORE **COMFORTABLE** GOING **OUT** THIS EVENING, SIR?

WHATEVER HAPPENS IN THE CITY TONIGHT, ALFRED, **CAPTAIN GORDON** AND HIS MEN CAN **HANDLE** IT.

I DARE SAY, I HOPE WE CAN AFFORD THE **ELECTRIC** BILL...

... I SCARCELY REMEMBER A TIME WHEN WE'VE HAD **THIS MANY** LIGHTS ON.

HELLO.

COOL...

TRICK OR TREAT!

I'll never truly und stand what happen to me last night.

What's more, I'm not certai I want to.

Clearly, someth had to be chang in my life.

And now... something has...